Series 563

A Ladybird
'LEARNING TO READ' Book

PUPPIES
AND
KITTENS

by M. E. GAGG, N.F.U.

with illustrations
by H. WOOLLEY

Ladybird Books   Loughborough

This puppy can see a frog.

This puppy
can see a robin.

This puppy
can see two mice.

This puppy
can see
two kittens.

These puppies
can see a snail.

What can
this puppy see?

This kitten

can see a spider

This kitten

can see a mouse

This kitten

wants some milk.

This kitten
has some milk.

This puppy
wants some dinne

This puppy has a bone.

This puppy wants to play with the chicks.

This puppy wants to play with the hedgehog.

This puppy
wants to play
with the trumpet

This kitten

wants to play

with the toys.

These kittens
want to write.

This puppy
has paint
on his paws.

This puppy has broken the doll.

This kitten
is in a sock.

This puppy
wants his bone.

This puppy does not want a bath.

This kitten does not want to get wet.

The kittens want
a bedtime story.
Goodnight kittens,
Goodnight puppies

Series 563